A Tale of Three Kings

A Study in Brokenness

A Tale of Three Kings

A Study in Brokenness

by Gene Edwards

CHRISTIAN BOOKS
AUGUSTA, MAINE

Dedication

To the brokenhearted Christians coming out
of authoritarian groups, seeking solace,
healing and hope. May you somehow
recover and go on with Him who is liberty.

And to Christians who have been, or
presently are, involved in the heart-rending
experience of a division within your
fellowship. May this story give you light,
clarity and comfort. And may you, too,
somehow recover and go on with Him who is
peace.

And may you both be so utterly healed that
you can still answer the call of Him who
asks for all because He is all.

Acknowledgement

To Helen, Carman and Patty for aiding in
the preparation of this manuscript; and to
Brad, who did the cover.

Preface to The Second Edition

When I first penned *A Tale of Three Kings*
I would have been encouraged to know it
would live long enough to go through two
or three printings. I utterly
underestimated the number of devastated
Christians out there. The book was
intended for a rather small audience,
Christians damaged by the authoritarian
movement. A far broader audience has
taken up this book, though. It is an
audience made up of Christians damaged
by church splits and by individual
"Christian to Christian" clashes.

I have been a little awed by the reception
of this book and the fact that the reception
was world-wide. The number of pastors
and Christian workers who have ordered
this book in bulk, to be passed out to their
people, has been only short of
phenomenal. That *A Tale of Three Kings*
has been turned into plays and has been
read publicly from pulpits turned awe to
amazement. Obviously there is a great
deal of pain and hurt out there in

Christendom that is rarely addressed or ministered to. I hope this book, *Letters to A Devastated Christian,* and *Our Mission* will become ministers to those needs.

Author's Preface

Why this book and what is its purpose?
The answer can probably be traced to my
postman. For some reason unknown to
me, I receive correspondence from
Christians all over the world. Some years
ago there began a growing number of
letters from Christians devastated by the
authoritarian movement which had
become so popular with many evangelical
groups. A reaction to this totalitarian
concept eventually set in. A mass exodus
was soon under way. The stories being
told by these spiritual fugitives are often
terrifying and sometimes unbelievable. I
am not at all sure if it is the doctrine itself
that is causing such widespread carnage
or the inordinate practice of this doctrine.
Whatever it is, in over thirty years as an
evangelical Christian minister, I have
never seen anything that has damaged so
many believers so deeply. The wreckage
appears to be universal and recovery from
it is almost nil.

This book reflects my concern for this
multitude of confused, brokenhearted and

often bitter Christians who now find their spiritual lives in shambles and who are groping about for even the slightest word of hope.

This emphasis on submission and authority in evengelical circles is a recent enough development that there has appeared little in the way of literature to balance or temper it. Certainly there is very little in print to comfort or counsel these virtually destroyed Christians. This book, I trust, will serve in some small way to meet this need. Frankly, the only other work I know to recommend is Orwell's little classic, *Animal Farm*. I urge—even implore—every reader of *A Tale of Three Kings* to read this book, too.

There is one thing, dear reader, this book is most certainly not intended to be. It is not intended to be additional fodder in your cannon to better blast your adversaries, whatever your view. I would beg you to be done with such ancient and brutish ways. This book is intended for individual healing and for private retreat.

This final word: *A Tale of Three Kings* has a companion volume entitled *Letters to a Devastated Christian*, which was

specifically penned to give practical
advice to Christians who have been
shipwrecked by conduct of other
Christians. I trust both volumes will
sound a note of hope, even if that note is
heard ever so distantly.

Gene Edwards

A Tale of
Three Kings

*They have set up kings, but not
by me: they have made princes, and
I know it not...Hosea 8:4*

Well, dear reader, how nice to be with you once more. It is a privilege to spend this time with you. Thank you for meeting here, and I suggest we hasten into the playhouse as I see that they have already dimmed the lights.

There are two seats reserved for us not too far from the stage. Quickly, let us take them.

I understand the story is a drama. I trust, though, you will not find it sad.

I believe we will find the story to be in two parts. In Part One we shall meet an older king, Saul by name, and a young shepherd boy called David. In Part Two we shall once more meet an older king and a young man. But this time the older king is David and the young man is Absalom.

The story is a portrait (you might prefer to call it a rough charcoal sketch) of submission and authority within the Kingdom of God.

Ah, they have turned off the lights, the players have taken their places. The audience has quieted itself. The curtain is rising.

Our story has begun.

Prologue

The almighty, living God turned to Gabriel and spoke thusly.

"Go, take these two portions of My being. There are two destinies waiting. To each of them give one portion of Myself."

Carrying two glowing, pulsating lights of Life, Gabriel opened the door into the realm between two universes and disappeared. He had stepped into The Mall of Unborn Destinies.

"I have here two portions of the nature of God. The first is the very cloth of His nature. When wrapped about you, it clothes you with the breath of God. As water surrounds one who is within the sea, so does His very breath envelop you. With this, *the wind that clothes*, you will have His power—power to subdue armies, shame the enemies of God and accomplish His work on the earth. Here is the power of God as a gift. Here is immersion into the Spirit."

A destiny stepped forward: "This portion of God is for me."

"True," replied the angel. "And remember, whoever receives such a great portion of power as this is will surely be known by many. Ere your earthly pilgrimage is done, your true character will be known; yea, even *revealed*, by means of this power. Such is the destiny of all who wear and wield this portion, for it touches only the outward man, affecting the inner man not one whit. Outward power will always unveil the inner resources, or the lack thereof."

The first destined one received and stepped back.

Gabriel spoke again.

"I have here the second of two elements of the Living God. This is not a gift but an inheritance. A gift is worn on the outer man; an inheritance is planted deep inside—like a seed. Yet, even though it is such a small planting, this planting grows and, in time, fills all the inner man."

Another destiny stepped forward. "I believe this element is to be mine for my earthly pilgrimage."

"True," responded the angel again. "I must tell you that what has been given you is a glorious thing—the only element in the universe known to God or angels that can change the human heart. Yet, even this very element of God cannot accomplish its task nor can it grow and fill your entire inner being unless it be compounded well. It must be mixed lavishly with pain, sorrow and crushing."

The second destined one received and stepped back.

Beside Gabriel sat the angel Recorder. He dutifully entered into his ledger the record of the two destinies.

"And who shall these destinies become after they go through the door to the visible universe?" asked Recorder.

Replied Gabriel softly, "Each, in his time, shall be king."

Part One

Chapter I

The youngest son of any family bears two distinctions: He is considered to be both spoiled and uninformed. Usually little is expected of him. Inevitably, he displays fewer characteristics of leadership than the other children in the family. He never leads, he only follows, for he has no one younger than he on whom to practice leadership.

So it is today. So it was three thousand years ago in a village called Bethlehem, in a family of eight boys. The first seven sons of Jesse worked near their father's farm. The youngest was sent on treks into the mountains to graze the family's small flock of sheep.

On those pastoral jaunts, this youngest son always carried two things: a sling and a small, guitar-like instrument. Spare time for a sheepherder is abundant on rich mountain plateaus where sheep graze for days in one sequestered meadow. But as time passed and days became weeks, the young man became very lonely. The feeling of friendlessness that always roamed around inside him was magnified. He often cried. He also played his harp a great deal. He had a good voice, so he often sang. When these activities failed to solace him, he gathered up a pile of stones and, one by one, swung them at a distant tree with something akin to fury.

When one rockpile was dissipated, he would walk to the blistered tree, reassemble his rocks and designate yet another leafy enemy at yet a farther distance.

He engaged in many such solitary battles.

This slingsman-singer-shepherd also loved his Lord. At night, when all the sheep lay sleeping, and he sat staring at the dying fire, he would strum upon his harp and break into a concert of one. He sang the ancient hymns of his forefathers' faith. While he sang, he wept, and while weeping he often broke forth in abandoned praise until mountains in distant places picked up his praise and tears and passed them on to higher mountains still, from whence they eventually were cast up to the ears of God.

When he did not praise and when he did not cry, he tended to each and every lamb and sheep. When not occupied with his flock, he swung his companionable sling and swung it again and again until he could tell every rock precisely where to go.

Once, while singing his lungs out to God, angels, sheep and passing clouds, he spied a living enemy: a huge bear! He lunged forward. Both found themselves moving furiously toward the same small object, a lamb feeding at a table of rich, green grass. Youth and bear stopped half way and whirled to face one another. Even as he instinctively searched into his pocket for a stone, the young man realized, "Why, I am not afraid."

Meanwhile, brown lightning on mighty, furry legs charged at him with foaming madness. Impelled by the strength of youth, he married rock to leather and soon a brook-smooth pebble whined through the air to meet that charge.

A few moments later, the man, not quite so young as a moment before, picked up the little ewe and said, "I am your shepherd and God mine."

And so, long into the night, he wove the day's saga into a song. He hurled that hymn to the skies again and again until he had taught the melody and words to every angel that had ears. They, in turn, became custodians of this wondrous song and passed it on as healing balm to brokenhearted men in every age to come.

Chapter II

A figure in the distance was running toward him. It grew and became his brother.

"Run!" cried the brother. "Run with all your strength. I'll watch the flock."

"Why?"

"An old man, a sage. He wants to meet all eight of the sons of Jesse and he has seen all but you."

"But why?"

"Run!"

David ran. He stopped long enough to get his breath. Then, sweat pouring down his sunburned cheeks, his red face matching his red curly hair, he walked into his father's house, his eyes recording everything in sight.

The youngest son of Jesse stood there, tall and strong, but more in the eyes of the curious old gentleman than anyone else in the room. Kin cannot always tell when a man is grown, even when looking straight at him. The elderly man saw. And something else, too. Some way the old man knew what God knew.

God had taken a house-to-house survey of the whole kingdom in search of something very special. As a result of this survey the Lord God Almighty had found that this leather-lunged troubadour loved his Lord with a purer heart than anyone else on all the sacred soil of Israel.

"Kneel," said the bearded one with the long, gray hair. Almost regally, for one who had never been in that particular position, he knelt, and felt oil pouring down upon his head. Somewhere in one of the closets of his mind labelled "childhood information," a thought was recalled: "This is what men do to make royalty! Samuel is making me a...what?"

The Hebrew words were unmistakable. Even children knew them.

"Behold the Lord's anointed!"

Quite a day for the life of that young man, wouldn't you say? Then do you find it strange that this most remarkable event led the young man, not to the throne, but to a decade of hellish agony and suffering? On that day, David was

6

enrolled, not into the lineage of royalty, but into the school of brokenness.

Samuel went home. The sons of Jesse, save one, went forth to war. The youngest, not yet ripe for war, did, nonetheless, receive a promotion in his father's home...from sheepherder to busboy. His new job now was to run food to his brothers on the front lines. He did this regularly.

On one such visit to the warfront, he killed another bear, in the exact same way as he had the first. This bear, however, was nine feet tall and human. As the result of this unusual feat, young David found himself a folk hero.

And eventually he found himself in the castle of a mad king. And in circumstances that were as insane as the king, the young man was to learn many indispensable things.

Chapter III

David sang to the mad king. Often. The music helped the old man a great deal, it seems. And all over the castle, when David sang, everyone stopped in the corridors of the king's palace, turned their ears in the direction of the king's chamber, and listened and wondered. How did such a young man come in possession of such wonderful words and music?

Everyone's favorite seemed to be the song the little lamb had taught him. They loved that song every bit as much as did the angels.

Nonetheless, the king was mad and, therefore, he was jealous. Or was it the other way around? Either way, the king felt threatened by David, as kings often do when there is a popular, promising young man beneath them. The king also knew, as did David, that this boy just might have his job some day.

But would David ascend to the throne by fair means or foul? Saul did not know. This question is one of the things that drove the king mad.

David was caught in a very uncomfortable position; however, within his circumstance he seemed to grasp a deep understanding of the unfolding drama in which he had been caught. He seemed to understand something that few of even the wisest men of his day understood. Something which even in our day, when men are wiser still, fewer understand.

And what was that?

God did not have, but wanted very much to have, men who would live in pain.

God wanted a broken vessel.

Chapter IV

The mad king saw David as a threat to
the *king's* kingdom. The king did not
understand, it seems, that God should be
left to decide what kingdoms survive
which threats. Not knowing this, Saul did
what all mad kings do. He threw spears at
David. He could. *He* was king. Kings can
do things like that. They almost always
do. Kings claim the right to throw spears.
Everyone knows such men have that
right. Everyone knows very, very well.
How do they know? Because the king has
told them so—many, many times.

Is it possible that this mad king was the
true king, even the Lord's anointed?

What about your king? Is he the Lord's
anointed? Maybe he is. Maybe he isn't. No
one can ever really know for sure. Men
say they are sure. Even *certain*. But they
are not. They do *not* know. God knows.
But *He* will not tell.

If your king is truly the Lord's anointed,
and if he *also* throws spears, then there
are some things you *can* know, and know
for sure:

Your king is quite mad.

And he is a king after the order of King Saul.

Chapter V

God has a university. It's a small school.
Few enroll, even fewer graduate. Very,
very few indeed.

God has this school because He does not
have broken men. Instead He has several
other types of men. He has men who claim
to be God's authority...and aren't; men
who claim to be broken...and aren't. And
men who *are* God's authority, but who are
mad *and* unbroken. And He has,
regretfully, a spectroscopic mixture of
everything in between. All of these He has
in abundance; but broken men, hardly at
all.

In God's sacred school of submission and
brokenness, why are there so few
students? Because all who are in this
school must suffer much pain. And as you
might guess, it is often the unbroken ruler
(whom god sovereignly picks) who metes
out the pain. David was once a student in
this school, and Saul was God's chosen
way to crush David.

As the king grew in madness, David grew

in understanding. He knew that God had placed him in the king's palace, under true authority.

The authority of King Saul, *true*? Yes, God's chosen authority. *Chosen for David.* Unbroken authority, yes. But divine in ordination, nonetheless.

Yes, *that* is possible.

David drew in his breath, placed himself under his mad king, and moved farther down the path of his earthly hell.

Chapter VI

David had a question: What do you do when someone throws a spear at you?

Does it not seem odd to you that David did not know the answer to this question? After all, everyone else in the world knows what to do when a spear is thrown at them. Why, you pick up the spear and throw it right back!

"When someone throws a spear at you, David, just wrench it right out of the wall and throw it back. Absolutely everyone else does, you can be sure."

And in doing this small feat of returning thrown spears, you will prove many things: You are courageous. You stand for the right. You boldly stand against the wrong. You are tough and can't be pushed around. You will not stand for injustice or unfair treatment. You are the defender of the faith, keeper of the flame, detector of all heresy. You will not be wronged. All of these attributes then combine to prove that you are also, obviously, a candidate for kingship. Yes, perhaps *you* are the Lord's anointed.

After the order of King Saul.

There is also a possibility that some 20 years after your coronation, *you* will be the most incredibly skilled spear thrower in all the realm. And, most assuredly, by then...

Quite mad.

Chapter VII

Unlike anyone else in spear-throwing history, David did *not* know what to do when a spear was thrown at him. He did not throw Saul's spears back at him. Nor did he make any spears of his own and throw them. Something was different about David. All he did was dodge.

What can a man, especially a young man, do when the king decides to use him for target practice? What if the young man decides not to return the compliment?

First of all, he must pretend he cannot see spears. Even when they are coming straight at him. Secondly, he must also learn to duck very quickly. Lastly, he must pretend nothing at all happened.

You can easily tell when someone has been hit by a spear. He turns a deep shade of bitter. David never got hit. Gradually, he learned a very well kept secret. He discovered three things that prevented him from ever being hit.

One, never learn anything about the fashionable, easily-mastered art of spear throwing. Two, stay out of the company of all spear throwers. And three, keep your mouth tightly closed.

In this way, spears will never touch you, even when they pierce your heart.

Chapter VIII

"My king is mad. At least, I perceive him so. What can I do?"

First, recognize this immutable fact: You cannot tell (none of us can) who is the Lord's anointed and who is not. Some kings, whom all will swear are after the order of King Saul, are really after the order of David. And others, whom all men swear are after the order of David, really belong to the order of King Saul. Who is correct? Who can know? To whose voice do you listen? *No man* is wise enough ever to break that riddle. All any of us can do is walk around asking ourselves the question:

"Is this man the Lord's anointed, and if so, is he after the order of Saul?"

Memorize that question very well. You may have to ask it of yourself 10,000 times. Especially if you are a citizen of a realm whose king just might be mad.

Asking this question may not seem difficult, but it is. Especially when you are crying very hard...and dodging spears...and being tempted to throw one back...and being encouraged by others to do just that. And all your rationality and sanity and logic and intelligence and common sense agree. But remember in your tears: You know only the question, not the answer.

No one knows the answer.

Except God.

And He *never* tells.

Chapter IX

"I did not like that last chapter. It skirted the problem. I'm in David's situation, and I am in agony. What do I do when the kingdom I'm in is ruled by a spear-wielding king? Should I leave? If so, how? Just what does a man *do* in the middle of a knife-throwing contest?"

Well, if you didn't like the question found in the last chapter, you won't like the answer found in this one.

The answer is, "You get stabbed to death."

"What is the necessity of that? Or the good of it?"

You have your eyes on the wrong King Saul. As long as you look at your king, you will blame him, and him alone, for your present hell. Be careful, for God has *His* eyes fastened sharply on another King Saul. Not the visible one standing up there throwing spears at you. No, God is looking at *another* King Saul. One just as bad—or worse.

God is looking at the King Saul in *you*.

"*In* me?!"

Saul is in your bloodstream, in the marrow of your bones. He makes up the very flesh and muscle of your heart. He is mixed into your soul. He inhabits the nuclei of your atoms.

King Saul is one with you.

You are King Saul!

He breathes in the lungs and beats in the breast of all of us. There is only one way to get rid of him. He must be annihilated.

You may not particularly find this to be a compliment, but at least now you know why God put you under someone who just *might* be King Saul.

David the sheepherder would have grown up to become King Saul II, except that God cut away the Saul inside David's heart. The operation, by the way, took years and was a brutalizing experience that almost killed the patient. And what were the scalpel and tongs God used to remove this inner Saul?

God used the outer Saul.

King Saul sought to destroy David, but his only success was that he became the handmaiden of God to put to death the Saul who roamed about in the caverns of David's own soul. Yes, it is true that David was virtually destroyed in the process, but this had to be. Otherwise the Saul in him would have survived.

David accepted this fate. He embraced the cruel circumstances. He lifted no hand, nor offered resistance. Nor did he grandstand his piety. Silently, privately, he bore the crucibles. Because of this he was deeply wounded. His whole inner being was mutilated. His personality was altered. When the gore was over, David was barely recognizable.

You weren't satisfied with the question in the last chapter? Then you probably didn't like the answer in this one.

None of us do.

Except God.

Chapter X

How does a man know when it is finally time to leave the Lord's anointed— especially the Lord's anointed after the order of King Saul?

David never made that decision. The Lord's anointed made it for him. The king's own decree settled the matter! "Hunt him down, kill him like a dog." Only then did David leave. No, he fled. Even then, he never spoke a word or lifted a hand against Saul. Please also note this: David did not split the kingdom when he made his departure. He did not take part of the population with him. He left *alone*.

Alone. *All* alone. King Saul II never does that. He always takes those who "insist on coming along."

Yes, men do insist on going with you, don't they? They are willing to help you found the kingdom of King Saul II.

Such men *never* dare leave alone.

But David left alone. You see, the Lord's true anointed can leave alone.

There's only *one* way to leave a kingdom:
Alone.

All alone.

Chapter XI

Caves are not the ideal place for morale building. There is a certain sameness to them all, no matter how many you have lived in. Dark. Wet. Cold. Stale. A cave becomes even worse when you are its sole inhabitant...and in the distance you can hear the dogs baying.

But sometimes, when the dogs and hunters were not near, the prey sang. He started low, then lifted up his voice and sang the song the little lamb had taught him. The cavern walls echoed each note just as the mountains once had done. The music rolled down into deep cavern darkness that soon became an echoing choir singing back to him.

He had less now than he had when he was a shepherd, for now he had no lyre, no sun, not even the company of sheep. The memories of the court had faded. David's greatest ambition now reached no higher than a shepherd's staff. *Everything* was being crushed out of him.

He sang a great deal.

And matched each note with a tear.

How strange, is it not, what suffering begets?

There in those caves, drowned in the sorrow of his song, and in the song of his sorrow, David very simply became the greatest hymn writer, and the greatest comforter of broken hearts this world shall ever know.

Chapter XII

He ran—through soggy fields and down
slimy riverbeds. Sometimes the dogs came
close; sometimes they even *found* him. But
swift feet, rivers, and watery pits hid him.
He took his food from the fields, dug roots
from the roadside, slept in trees, hid in
ditches, crawled through briars and mud.
For days he ran—not daring to stop or eat.
He drank the rain. Half naked, all filthy,
on he walked, stumbled, crawled and
clawed.

Caves were castles now. Pits were home.

In times past, mothers had always told
their children that if they did not behave
they would end up like the town drunk. No
longer. They had a better, more
frightening story. "Be good, or you'll end
up like the giant killer."

In Jerusalem, when men taught of being
submissive to kings and honoring the
Lord's anointed, David was the parable.
"See, this is what God does to rebellious
men." The young listeners shuddered at
the thought and somberly resolved never
to have anything to do with rebellion.

So it was then, so it is now, so shall it ever be.

Much later, David would reach a foreign land, and a small, very small, measure of safety. Here, too, he was feared, hated, lied about and plotted against. He shook hands with murder on several occasions.

These were David's darkest hours. You know them as his pre-king days, but he didn't. He assumed this was his lot forever.

Suffering was giving birth. Humility was being born.

By earthly measures he was a shattered man; by heaven's measure, a broken one.

Chapter XIII

Others had to flee as the king's madness grew. First one, then three, then ten, and eventually hundreds. After long searching, some of these fugitives made contact with David. They had not seen him for a long time.

The truth was that when they did see him again, they simply didn't recognize him. He had changed; his personality, his disposition, his total being had been altered. He talked less. He loved God more. He sang differently. They had never heard these songs before. Some were lovely beyond words, but some could freeze the blood in your veins.

Those who found him and who decided to be his fellow fugitives were a sorry, worthless lot: thieves, liars, complainers, fault-finders, rebellious men with rebellious hearts. They were blind with hate for the king and, therefore, for all authority figures. They would have been troublemakers in paradise, if ever they could have gotten in.

David did not lead them. He did not share

their attitudes. Yet, unsolicited, they began to follow him.

He never spoke to them of authority. He never spoke of submission; but, to a man, they submitted. He laid down no rules. Legalism is not a word found in the vocabulary of fugitives. Nonetheless, they cleaned up their outward lives. Gradually, their inward lives began to change, too.

They didn't fear submission or authority; they didn't even think about the topic, much less discuss it. Then why did they follow him? They didn't, exactly. It was just that he was...well...David. That didn't need explanation.

And so, for the first of two times, true kingship had its nativity.

Chapter XIV

"Why, David, why?"

The place was another nameless cave.

The men stirred about restlessly.
Gradually, and very uneasily, they began
to settle in. All were as confused as Joab,
who had finally voiced their questions.

Joab wanted some answers. Now!

David should have seemed embarrassed
or at least defensive. He was neither. He
was looking past Joab like a man viewing
another realm which only he could see.

Joab walked directly in front of David,
looked down on him, and began roaring
his frustrations.

"Many times he almost speared you to
death in his castle. I've seen that with my
own eyes. Finally, you ran away. Now for
years you have been nothing but a rabbit
for him to chase. Furthermore, the whole
world believes the lies he tells about you.
He has come, the King himself, hunting
every cave, pit and hole on earth to find
you and kill you like a dog. But tonight

you had *him* at the end of his own spear and you did nothing!

"Look at us. We're animals *again*. Less than an hour ago you could have freed us all. Yes, we could all be free, right now! Free! And Israel, too. She would be free. Why, David, why did you not end these years of misery?"

There was a long silence. Men shifted again, uneasily. They were not accustomed to seeing David rebuked.

"Because," said David very slowly (and with a gentleness that seemed to say, 'I heard what you asked, but not the way you asked it'), "because once, long ago, he was not mad. He was young. He was great. Great in the eyes of God and men. And it was God who made him king— God—not men."

Joab blazed back, "But now he is *mad!* And God is no longer with him. And, David, he will yet kill you!"

This time it was David's answer that blazed with fire.

"Better he kill me than I learn his ways. Better he kill me than I become as he is. I shall not practice the ways that cause kings to go mad. I will not throw spears, nor will I allow hatred to grow in my heart. I will not avenge. Not now. Not ever!"

Joab could not handle such a senseless answer. He stormed out into the dark.

That night men went to bed on cold, wet stone and muttered about their leader's distorted, masochistic views of relationships to kings, especially mad ones.

Angels went to bed that night too, and dreamed, in the afterglow of that rare, rare day, that God might yet be able to give His authority to a trustworthy vessel.

Chapter XV

What kind of man was Saul? Who was this one who made himself David's enemy? Anointed of God. Deliverer of Israel. And yet remembered mostly for his madness.

Forget the bad press. Forget the stinging reviews. Forget his reputation. Look at the facts. Saul was one of the greatest figures of human history. He was a farm boy, a real country kid. He was tall, good-looking and well-liked.

He was baptized into the Spirit of God.

He also came from a good family; that is, in his lineage were some of the great historical figures of all mankind. Abraham, Israel, Moses, these were his ancestors.

Do you remember the background? Abraham had founded a nation. Moses had set that nation free from slavery. Joshua gave those people a toehold in the land which was promised to them by God. The judges kept the whole thing from disintegrating into total chaos. That's when Saul came along. It was Saul who took these people and welded them into a united kingdom.

Saul united a people and founded a kingdom. Few men have ever done that. He created an army out of thin air. He won battles in the power of God, defeated the enemy again and again, as few men ever have. Remember that, and remember too, that this man was immersed in the Spirit. Furthermore, he was a prophet. The Spirit came on him in power and authority. He did and said unprecedented things and it was all by the power of the Spirit resting on him.

He was everything men today are seeking to be...empowered with the Holy Spirit...able to do the impossible...for God. A leader, chosen by God with power from God.

Saul was given authority that is God's alone. He was God's anointed and God treated him that way.

He was also eaten with jealousy, capable of murder and willing to live in spiritual darkness.

Is there a moral in these contradictions? Yes, and it will splinter a lot of your concepts about power, about great men under God's anointing, and about God Himself.

Many men pray for the power of God. More every year. Those prayers sound powerful, sincere, godly and without ulterior motive. Hidden under such prayer and fervor, however, are ambition, a craving for fame, the desire to be considered a spiritual giant. The man who prays such prayer may not even know it, but such dark motives and desires are in his heart...in *your* heart.

Even as men pray these prayers, they are hollow inside. There is little internal spiritual growth. Prayer for power is the quick and the short way, circumnavigating internal growth.

There is a vast difference between the outward clothing of the Spirit's power and the inward filling of the Spirit's life. In the first, despite the power, the hidden man of the heart may remain unchanged. In the latter, that monster is dealt with.

Interesting about God. He hears all those requests for power, which fervent young men pray (in every generation) and He answers them! Very often He grants those requests for power, for authority. Sometimes in answering them, He says "yes" to some very unworthy vessels.

He gives unworthy men power? His power? Even though they are a pile of dead men's bones inside?

Why does God do such a thing? The answer is both simple and shocking. He sometimes gives unworthy vessels a greater portion of power so that it might eventually be revealed for all to see the *true* state of internal nakedness within that man.

So think again when you hear the power merchant. Remember: God sometimes gives power to men for unseen reasons. A man can be living in the grossest of sin and the outward gift will still be working perfectly. The gifts of God, once given, cannot be recalled. Even in the presence of sin. Furthermore, some men, living just such lives, *are* the Lord's anointed...in the Lord's eyes. Saul was living proof of this fact.

The gifts cannot be revoked. Terrifying, isn't it?

If you are young and have never seen such things, you may be certain that sometime in the next 40 years you will see. Highly gifted and very powerful men... reputed to be leaders in the Kingdom of God, do some very dark and ugly deeds.

What does this world need: Gifted men, outwardly empowered? Or broken men, inwardly transformed?

Keep in mind that some of the men who have been given the very power of God have raised armies, defeated the enemy, brought forth mighty works of God, preached and prophesied with unparalleled power and eloquence...

And thrown spears,

And hated other men,

And attacked other men,

And plotted to kill,

And prophesied naked,

And even consulted witches.

Chapter XVI

"You still haven't answered my question. The man I sit under: I think he is a King Saul. How can I know with certainty?"

It is not given to us to know. And remember, even Sauls are often the Lord's anointed.

You see, there are always men— everywhere, in every age, and in every group—who will stand and tell you: "That man is after the order of King Saul." While another, just as sure, will rise to declare, "No, he is the Lord's anointed after the order of David." No man can *really* know which of the two is correct. And if you happen to be in the balcony looking down at those two men screaming at one another, you may wonder to which order, if any, *they* belong.

Remember, your leader may be a David.

"That's impossible!"

Is it? Most of us know at least two men in the lineage of David who have been damned and crucified by men. Men who were absolutely certain the men they were crucifying were *not* Davids.

And if you don't know of two such cases, for sure you know of one.

Men who go after the Sauls among us often crucify the Davids among us.

Who, then, can know who is a David and who is a Saul?

God knows. But He won't tell.

Will you be so certain your king is a Saul and not a David that you are willing to take the position of God and do war against your Saul? If so, then let us thank God you did not live in the days when Golgotha was in use.

What, then, can you do? Very little. Perhaps nothing.

However, the passing of time (and the behavior of your leader while that time passes) reveals a great deal about your leader.

And the passing of time, and the way you react to that leader—be he David or Saul—reveals a great deal about *you*.

Chapter XVII

Two generations after the reign of Saul, a young man enthusiastically enrolled himself into the ranks of Israel's army under a new king, the grandson of David. He soon began hearing tales of David's mighty men of valor. He determined to discover if one of those mighty men might still be alive and, if so, to find him and talk to him, though he calculated that such a man would be over a hundred years in age.

At last he discovered that, sure enough, one such man still lived. Having learned of his whereabouts, the youth made haste to his dwelling. Anxiously, if not hesitantly, he knocked on the door. Slowly it opened. There stood a giant of a man, gray...no, white haired...and wrinkled beyond expectation.

"Are you, sir, one of David's mighty men of long ago—one of these men of whom we have heard so much?"

The old man surveyed the young man's face, his features, his uniform, for a long moment. Then, in an ancient but firm voice, he replied, never taking his steady gaze off the young man's face.

"If you are asking if I am a former thief and cave dweller and one who followed a sobbing, hysterical fugitive, then yes, I was one of the 'mighty men of David.'"

He straightened his shoulders with those last words; nonetheless, his sentence ended in a chuckle.

"Why, you make the Great King sound like a weakling. Was he not the greatest of all rulers?"

"He was no weakling," said the old man. Then, sizing up the motivation for the eager young man's presence at his door, he replied wisely and softly, "Nor was he a great leader."

"Then what, good sir? For I have come to learn the ways of the Great King and his... uh...mighty men. What *was* the greatness of David?"

"I see you have the ambitions typical of youth," said the old warrior. "I have the distinct notion you dream of leading men yourself one day." He paused, then continued reflectively. "Yes, I'll tell you of the greatness of my king, but my words may surprise you."

The old man's eyes filled with tears as he thought first of David and then of the foolish new king only recently crowned.

"I will tell you of my king and his greatness.

"My king has never threatened me as does yours. Your new king has begun his reign with laws, rules, regulations and fear. The clearest memory I have of my king, when we lived in the caves, is that his was a life of *submission*. Yes, David showed me submission, *not* authority. He taught me, not the quick cures of rules and laws, but the art of patience. *That* is what changed my life. Legalism is nothing but a leader's way of avoiding suffering.

"Rules were invented by elders, so they could get to bed early! Men who harp on authority only prove they have none. And kings who make speeches about submission only betray twin fears in their hearts: They are not certain they are really true leaders, sent of God. *And* they live in mortal fear of a rebellion.

"My king spoke not of submitting to him.

He feared no rebellion...because...because he did not mind if he was dethroned!

"David taught me losing, not winning. Giving, not taking. He showed me that the leader, not the follower, is inconvenienced. He shielded us from suffering; he did not mete it out.

"He taught me that authority yields to rebellion, especially when that rebellion is nothing more dangerous than immaturity, or perhaps stupidity." The old man was obviously remembering some very tense and perhaps humorous episodes in the caves.

"No," he said, now in a voice with a touch of eloquence, "authority from God is not afraid of challengers, makes no defense, and cares not one whit if it must be dethroned.

"That was the greatness of the Gre...of the *true* King."

The old man began to walk away. Both anger and regality were evident in his bearing as he turned. Then he faced the youth once more, thundering one last salvo: "As far as David's having authority: Men who don't have it talk about it all the time. Submit, submit, that's all you hear. David had authority, but I don't think that fact ever occurred to him! We were 600 no-goods with a leader who cried a lot. That's all we were!"

Those were the last words the young soldier heard from the old warrior. Slipping back into the street, he wondered if he would ever again be happy serving under Rehoboam.

Chapter XVIII

So, having come to the end of our study of
Saul and David, you feel you have been
greatly assisted? What's that? You are
now certain the man you are under is not
truly from God...or if he is, he is at best
only a Saul? My, how certain we mortals
can be...of things even angels do not
know.

May I ask you then, what you plan to do
with this newly acquired knowledge? Yes,
I am aware that you yourself are neither a
Saul nor a David...but only a peasant of
the realm. You do plan, though, to share
your new discoveries with a few friends? I
see. Perhaps then, I should warn you that
with this heady new knowledge of yours
there is an inherent danger. A strange
mutation can take place within your own
heart. You see, it is possible...but wait!

What is it I see over there! There! In that
distant mist behind you. Turn. Do you
see? Who is that apparition-like figure
making his way through the fog? It seems
I have surely seen him before.

Look closely. Is it not possible for us to make out what he is doing?

He appears to be bending over some ancient chest. Yes, he has opened it.

Who is he? And what *is* he doing?

He has drawn something out of the chest. A cloak? It is some kind of cape. Why, he is putting it on! The thing fits him perfectly, falling about his shoulders like a mantle.

Now what? He reaches again into that chest. I know I have seen that person somewhere before. What is it he pulls forth this time? A shield? No, a coat of arms. Yes, a coat of arms from some ancient, long forgotten order. He holds it up as one who would make that order his own! Who is that man! The bearing. The stance. The carriage. I've seen it before. I'm sure.

Ah! He has moved out of the mist into the light. We will see him clearly now.

That face. Is it not you?!

Yes. It is. It is *you*! You who can so wisely discern the presence of an unworthy Saul!

Go! Look in yon mirror. That man is *you*!

Look, too, at the name upon that coat of arms.

Behold: ABSALOM THE SECOND!!!

Chapter XIX

"Look. Here comes David!"

Bright smiles, a few giggles, some light laughter.

"See! It's David, no less."

Again, wide grins, a wave, and quiet amusement.

"That isn't David," exclaimed a youth to his guardian as the two of them walked along the side of the street. "Why do they speak that way? That man is *not* David!"

"True, child, it is not David. It's only Absalom coming from the gate."

"Why do they call him David?" the boy asked, looking back over his shoulder at the handsome man in the chariot with the 50 men running before him.

"Because he reminds us all of David when he was young. And because we are all so glad there is such a fine young man to take David's place someday. And perhaps, too, because Absalom is even better looking than David. He may be the most handsome man alive."

"Will Absalom be king soon? How old is David, anyway? Is he about to die?"

"Of course not, my boy. Let's see...how old is David? Probably about the same age as King Saul when his reign came to an end."

"How old is Absalom?"

"About the same age as David when Saul was trying so hard to kill him."

"David is Saul's age. Absalom is the age of David when he first became king," mused the boy. They walked on silently for a while. The boy, obviously deep in thought, spoke again.

"Saul was very hard on David, was he not?"

"Yes, very."

"Is King David going to treat Absalom the same way? Will David be hard on Absalom?"

The guardian paused to consider the question, but the child went on: "If David treats Absalom badly, will Absalom behave with as much grace as did David?"

"Child, the future will surely tell us. My,

you ask such questions! If, when you are grown, you can give answers as well as you can now ask questions, you will surely be known as the wisest man on earth."

The two turned into the palace gate.

Chapter XX

It warmed your heart to know a man who saw things so clearly. Discerning. Yes, that was the word that best described him—discerning. He could penetrate to the heart of any problem.

Men felt secure just being with him. They even longed to have time with him. Talking with him, they realized that they themselves were wiser than they'd realized. Such a revelation made them feel good. As he discussed problem after problem and solution after solution, men began to long for the day when this one would be their leader. He could right so many wrongs. He gave them a sense of hope.

But this imposing, insightful man would never deliberately hasten the day of his own rule, of this they were certain. He was far too humble, too respectful of the present leader. Those around him began to feel a little frustrated that they would have to keep waiting for the better days of this man's rule.

The more they sat in his living room and talked, the more they realized there were things presently amiss in the kingdom. Yes, things amiss which they had never thought of before. And problems. Problems were coming to light they had never dreamed of. Yes, they really were growing in wisdom and in insight.

As the days passed, more and more of them came to listen. Word spread quietly. "Here is one who understands and has the answers." The frustrated came. They listened. They asked questions. They received excellent answers and began to hope.

Heads nodded. Dreams were born. As time passed, there were more such gatherings. Ideas turned into stories, stories of injustice that others might have deemed trivial. But not this listener! He was compassionate. And as those around him talked, the discovered injustices seemed to grow in number and severity. With each new story, men were more shocked at unfairness that was now, it seemed, rampant.

But the wise young man sat quietly and added not a word to these murmurings. He was too noble, you see. He always closed the evening conversations with an humble word of deference toward those with responsibilty...

But it was too much to expect that any man could sit quietly by forever. This endless parade of injustice was bound to stir even the most respectful man. Even the purest in heart would be smitten with anger. (And this man was certainly the very purest in heart!)

Such a compassionate man could not forever turn his face from these sufferings nor forever remain silent. Such noble character as this had someday to speak out.

Finally his followers, which he vowed he did not have, were almost livid. Their insights into the wrongdoings of the kingdom not only grew but abounded. They all wanted to do something about these endless injustices.

At last, it seemed, the magnificent young man might concede. At the outset it was only a word. Later, a sentence. Men's hearts leaped. Glee, if not joy, reigned. Nobility was at last arousing itself to action. But no! He cautioned them not to misunderstand. He was grieved, yes, but he could not speak against those in seats of responsibility. No, absolutely not. No matter how great the grievances, no matter how justified. He would *not*.

Yet he grieved more and more. It was obvious that some reports drove him to agony. Finally, his righteous anger broke out in cool, controlled words of strength. "These things ought not to be." He stood, eyes blazing. "If I were in responsibility, this is what I would do..."

And with these words, the rebellion was ignited. Ignited in all but one, that is. In the noblest and purest man in the room, this was not the case.

Rebellion had been in his heart for years.

Chapter XXI

"Sage!"

"Yes."

"Sage, may I have a moment of your time?"

"Why, of course, I have a great deal of time."

"You have just come from a gathering of friends at Absalom's home?"

"Yes, that is correct."

"Would you mind sharing some of the impressions you had while there?"

"You mean a general impression of Absalom and his friends?"

"Yes, that would be good enough."

"Well, I have met many men like Absalom. Many."

"Then what is he like?"

"He is both sincere and ambitious. A contradiction, perhaps, but true, nonetheless. He probably means some of what he says. But his ambition will continue long after he discovers his inability to do the things he promises. Righting the wrongs always becomes secondary to ascent to power."

"I'm sorry, Sage, I do not understand."

"Two things stand out in my mind. At one gathering, when Absalom was answering questions, he was very emphatic that there should be more freedom in the kingdom. Everyone liked that. 'A people should be led only by God, and not by men,' he said. 'Men should do only what they feel led of God to do. We should follow God, not a man.' I believe those were his words.

"At another meeting he spoke of the great visions he had for God's kingdom—of the great achievements the people were capable of. On the other hand, he spoke of many changes he would make in the way the kingdom is run. Although he did not seem to notice it, he had stated two irreconcilable propositions. Many changes, more freedom.

"Yes, indeed, he does remind me of many other men I have encountered over the passing years."

"Sage, I think I understand what you've said, but I'm not sure what your point is."

"Absalom dreams. Dreams of what should be, of what *will* be: 'This is what *I* will do,' he says. But to fulfill those dreams, he must have the people's cooperation. Ah, this is the point men overlook. Such dreams rest totally on the premise that the people of God will be with the new leader, that *all* will see as he sees. Such men can envision no problems in their own future kingdom. Possibly the people *will* follow, and, possibly, they will not.

"At most, the Lord's people will follow a leader for a few days. They are never with anyone very long. Generally, people do what they please. They can be stopped to do someone else's pleasure for a time, but not for long. People will not work too hard, even if they are following *God*.

"What will Absalom do when people stop following *him* willingly? Ah, now there is a question.

"You see, there is no kingdom without discord. Even God had His critics in heaven, you know. All kingdoms follow a bumpy course. And people, especially God's people, never follow any dream in unison. No, to accomplish all he spoke of tonight will take time. Not all will be willing to go along. Will he still be determined to put all his dreams into being? If so, then Absalom has but one recourse: dictatorship. Either that, or he will see few, if any, of his grand dreams accomplished. If he does become a dictator, I can assure you that in the not too distant future there will be discontent with *him*, just as there is now with the present king. Yes, if Absalom becomes king, soon thereafter you will be seeing new meetings such as the one we have just come from tonight...only with new faces, new dreams, and plans for a new rebellion, this one *against* Absalom! Then when *Absalom* hears of such a meeting, and of discussion about a rebellion, he will have but one recourse."

"What do you feel he will do, Sage?"

"Rebels who ascend the throne by rebellion have no patience with other rebels and their rebellions. When Absalom is faced with rebellion, he will become a tyrant. He will be ten times the evil he now sees in your king. He will squelch rebellion and rule with an iron hand...and by fear. He will eliminate all opposition.

This is always the final stage of high-sounding rebellions. Such will be Absalom's way if he takes the throne from David."

"But Sage, have not some rebellions been of benefit, throwing out brutes and despots?"

"Oh, yes, a few. But I remind you: This particular kingdom is different from all others. This kingdom is composed of God's people. It is a spiritual kingdom. I tell you emphatically, no rebellion in the kingdom of God is proper, nor can it ever be fully blessed."

"Why do you say this, Sage?"

"For many reasons. One is obvious. In the spiritual realm, a man who will lead a rebellion has already proven, no matter how grandiose his words or angelic his ways, that he has a critical nature, an unprincipled character, and hidden motives in his heart. Frankly, he is a thief. He creates dissatisfaction and tension within the realm, and then either seizes power or siphons off followers. The followers he gets, he uses to found his own dominion. Such a sorry beginning, built on the foundation of insurrection...No, God never honors division in His realm.

"I find it curious that men who feel qualified to split God's kingdom do not feel capable of going somewhere else, to another land, to raise up a completely new kingdom. No, they must steal from another leader. I have never seen the exception. They seem always to need at least a few pre-packaged followers.

"Beginning empty-handed and alone frightens the best of men. It also speaks volumes of just how sure they are that God is with them. Their every word, if seen true, tells of their insecurity.

"There are many lands unspoiled and unpossessed. There are many people in other places waiting to follow a true king, a true man of God. I repeat myself. (There are those who say I often repeat myself.) Why don't 'would-be kings and prophets' simply walk quietly away, alone, find another people in another place, and there raise up the kingdom they envision?

"Men who lead rebellions in the spiritual world are unworthy men. There are no exceptions. And now I must go. I must join the passing parade."

"Tell me, Sage, what is your name?"

"My name? I am History."

Chapter XXII

David stood looking over the balcony of the gardened terrace of his palace. The lights from the houses in the Holy City twinkled below him. From behind, a man approached. David sighed and, without turning, spoke. "Yes, Joab, what is it?"

"Do you know?"

"I know," he replied quietly.

"How long have you known?" asked Joab with anxious surprise.

"For months, years, perhaps a decade. Perhaps I have known for thirty years."

Joab was not sure, after this answer, if they were speaking of the same subject. Absalom, after all, was not much past thirty. "Sir, I speak of Absalom," he said a little hesitantly.

"As do I," said the king.

"If you have known so long, why did you not stop him?"

"I was just asking myself that same question."

"Shall I stop him for you?"

David whirled round! In one instant, Joab's query had resolved his dilemma.

"You shall not! Nor shall you speak one word to him. Nor shall you criticize him. Nor shall you allow anyone else to speak critically of him or what he is doing. Certainly you shall not stop him."

"But will he not then take the kingdom?"

David sighed again, softly, slowly. For a moment he balanced between tears and a smile. Then he smiled lightly and said, "Yes, perhaps he will."

"What will you do? Do you have plans?"

"No. None. Quite frankly, I have no idea what to do. I have fought many battles and faced many sieges. I have usually known what to do. But for this occasion, I have only the experience of my youth to draw on. The course I followed at that time seems to me to be the best I can follow now."

"And what course was that?"

"To do absolutely nothing."

Chapter XXIII

David was alone again. Slowly, quietly, he walked the length of his roof garden. Finally he paused and spoke aloud to himself.

"I have waited, Absalom; I have waited and watched for years. I have asked again and again, 'What is in the heart of this young man?' And now I know. You will do the unthinkable. You will divide, Absalom, the very kingdom of God. All else was talk."

David was quiet for a moment. Then, almost in awe, he spoke, his voice hushed. "Absalom does not hestitate to divide the *Kingdom of God.*

"Now I know. He seeks followers. At least he does not turn them away! Though he seems magnificently pure and illustriously noble, still he divides. His followers grow, even though he convincingly states that he has none."

For a long time David said nothing. Finally, with a trace of humor in his words, he began to address himself. "All right, good King David, you have one issue resolved. You are in the middle of a division and you may very well be dethroned. Now, to the second issue." He paused, lifted his hand and, almost fatally, asked, "What *will* you do?

"The kingdom hangs in the balance. It seems I have two choices: to lose everything, or to be a Saul. I can stop Absalom. I need only to be a Saul. In my old age, shall I now become a Saul? I feel the Lord Himself awaits my decision.

"Shall I now be a Saul?" he asked himself again, this time loudly.

A voice from behind answered, " Good king, he has been no David to you."

David turned. It was Abishai who had approached unannounced.

"A crowded place, this terrace," quipped David.

"Sir?" said Abishai.

"Nothing. Suffice it to say I have not been without visitors today—a day when I would have chosen solitude. What did you say to me? In fact, what did I say?"

"You said, 'Shall I be a Saul to Absalom?'

and I replied, 'He has been no young David to you.'"

"I never challenged Saul; I never attempted to divide the kingdom during his reign. Is that what you are saying?"

"More," replied Abishai strongly. "Saul was evil toward you and made your life torture. You responded only with respect and private agony. The bad things which happened in that day came only from one side. All fell on you. Yet you could have divided the kingdom and probably could have overthrown Saul. Rather than do that, you packed up and left the kingdom. You fled rather than cause division. You risked your life for unity and sealed your lips and eyes to all his injustices. You had more cause to rebel than any man in the history of this or any other kingdom that ever has been or ever shall be. Absalom has to twist hard to conjure up his list of injustices...few of them significant, I might add. Has Absalom behaved as you did? Absalom respecting you? Absalom seeking to preserve the Kingdom? Absalom refusing to speak against you? Absalom refusing followers? Absalom departing the land to prevent its sundering? Absalom respectful? Absalom

bearing suffering in silent agony? The
bad things falling on Absalom?

"No, he is only pure and noble!"

Abishai's last words came out almost in
bites. Then he continued again, more
gravely this time.

"His grievances are minor compared to
your rightful grievances toward Saul. You
never mistreated Saul. And you have
never, in any way, been unfair to
Absalom."

David interrupted with a grin. "I seem to
have a gift for making old men and young
men hate me without a cause. In my
youth, the old attack me; when I am old,
the young attack me. What a marvelous
achievement."

"My point," continued Abishai, "is that
Absalom is no David. Therefore I ask you:
Why don't you stop his rebellion? Stop
him, the miserable..."

"Careful, Abishai. Remember he is also a
son of the king. We should never speak ill
of the son of a king."

"Good king, I remind you that you refused
to raise your sword or your spear even
once against Saul. I repeat myself.

74

Absalom speaks against you night and day. He will one day—soon—raise an army against you. Nay, a nation. *This* nation! Young Absalom is no young David. I counsel you to stop him!"

"You are asking me, Abishai, to become a Saul," David replied heavily.

"No, I'm saying he is no David; stop him!"

"And if I stop him, will I still be a David? If I stop him, will I not be Saul?" asked the king, his eyes piercing Abishai. "Abishai, to stop him, I must either be a Saul or an Absalom."

"My king and my friend, I speak to you fondly: I sometimes think you are a bit insane."

"Yes, I can see why," chuckled David.

"Dear king, Saul was a bad king. Absalom is in some ways, a youthful reincarnation of Saul. You only are constant. You are forever the brokenhearted shepherd boy. Tell me truthfully, what do you plan?"

"Until now, I have not been sure. Of this I am now certain: In my youth I was no Absalom. In my old age I shall not be a Saul. In my youth, by your own words, I was David. In my old age I intend to be David still. Even if it costs me a throne, a kingdom, and perhaps my head."

Abishai said nothing for a while. Then, slowly, he spoke, making sure he grasped the significance of David's decision.

"You were not an Absalom; you will not be a Saul. Sir, if you are not willing to put Absalom down, then I suggest we prepare to evacuate the kingdom, for Absalom will surely rule."

"Only as surely as King Saul killed the shepherd boy," replied the wise old king.

"What?" said Abishai, startled.

"Think on it, Abishai. God once delivered a defenseless shepherd boy from the powerful, mad king. He can yet deliver an old ruler from an ambitious young rebel."

"You underestimate your adversary," retorted Abishai.

"You underestimate my God," replied David serenely.

"But why, David? Why not fight?"

"I will give you the answer. If you will recall—for you were there—I once gave this same answer to Joab in a cave long ago!

"It is better I be defeated, even killed, than to learn the ways of...of a Saul, *or* the ways of an Absalom. The kingdom is not *that* valuable. Let him have it, if that be the Lord's will. I repeat: I *shall not* learn the ways of either Sauls or Absaloms.

"And now, being an old man, I will add a word I might not have known then. Abishai, no man knows his own heart. I certainly do not know mine. Only God does. Shall I defend my little realm in the name of God? Shall I throw spears, and plot and divide...and kill men's spirits if not their bodies...to protect *my* empire? I did not lift a finger to be *made* king. Nor to preserve a kingdom. Even the Kingdom of God! God put me here. It is not my responsibility to take, or *keep* authority. Do you not realize, it may be *His* will for these things to take place? I suspect that, if He chose, God could protect and keep the kingdom even now. After all, it is *His* kingdom.

"As I said, no man knows his heart. I do not know mine. Who knows what is really in my heart? It may be that in God's eyes I am no longer worthy to rule. Perhaps He *is* through with me. Perhaps it is His will for Absalom to rule. I honestly don't know. But if this is His will, I wish it. God may be finished with me!

"Any young rebel who raises his hand against one whom he believes to be a Saul; any old king who raises his hand against one whom he believes to be an Absalom, may—in truth—be raising his hand against the will of God.

"In either case, I shall raise no hand! Wouldn't I look a little strange trying to stay in control when God was desiring that I fall?"

"But you know that Absalom should not be king!" replied Abishai in frustration.

"Do I? No man knows. Only God knows, and He has not spoken. I will not fight to be king or to remain king. May God come tonight and take the throne, the kingship and..." David's voice faltered, "and His *anointing* from me. I seek his will, not His power. I repeat. I desire his will more than I desire a position of leadership. He may be through with me."

"King David," came a voice from behind the two men.

"Yes? Oh, a messenger. What is it?"

"Absalom. He wishes to see you a

moment. He wishes to ask permission to go to Hebron to make a sacrifice."

"David," said Abishai hoarsely, "you know what that really means, don't you?"

"Yes."

"And you know what he will do if you let him go?"

"Yes."

David turned to the messenger. "Tell Absalom I will be there momentarily."

David looked one last time at the quiet city below, turned, and walked toward the door.

"*Will* you let him go to Hebron?" Abishai demanded.

"I will," said the king of all kings. "Yes, I will."

Then he turned to the messenger. "This is a dark hour for me. When I have finished speaking to Absalom, I shall retire. Tomorrow have one of the prophets come to me for consultation. Or a scribe. On second thought, send me Zadok, the high priest. Ask him if he would join me here after the evening sacrifice."

Abishai called out once more, softly this time. Admiration flashed across his face. "Good king, thank you."

"For doing what?" the puzzled king asked as he turned back in the doorway.

"Not for what you have done, but for what you have *not* done. Thank you for *not* throwing spears, for not rebelling against kings, for not exposing a man in authority when he was so very vulnerable, for not dividing a kingdom, for not attacking young Absaloms who look very much like young Davids, but are not."

He paused. "And thank you for suffering, for being willing to lose everything. Thank you for giving God a free hand to end, and even destroy, your Kingdom—if it pleases Him. Thank you for being an example to us all.

"And most of all," he chuckled, "thanks for not consulting witches."

Chapter XXIV

"Nathan!"

"What...? Oh, it is you, Zadok."

"You will pardon my intrusion, but I have been observing you for several moments now. You were about to enter the throne room, I believe, to see the King?"

"Yes, Zadok. That was my intent, but I have thought better of it. The king has no need of me."

"I am disappointed, Nathan. In my judgment the king has great need of you. He is facing the gravest test of his life. I am not at all sure he can pass a test so demanding as is this one."

"He has *already* passed this test, Zadok," countered Nathan with a sureness in his voice that assented to the truth that he was a prophet of God.

"Already passed this test? Forgive me, Nathan, but I have no idea of what you speak. This crisis, as you well know, has only begun."

"Zadok, your king passed *this* test long ago, when he was a young man.

"You speak of Saul? But that, my friend, was a wholly different matter."

"Not at all. It is *exactly* the same. There is really no difference at all. As David related to his God and to the man over him in that hour long ago...so now will David also relate to his God and the man under him. There can be no difference. Not ever.

"True, circumstances may be altered... slightly. Ever so slightly, I might add. But the heart...! Ah, the heart is always the same.

"Zadok, I have always been grateful Saul was our *first* king. I shudder to think of the trouble he might have caused if, as a young man, he had found himself under some other king. There is no real difference between the man who discovers he has a Saul in his life and the man who finds he has an Absalom in his. In either situation, the corrupt heart will find its 'justification.' The Sauls of this world can never see a David; they can only see Absalom. The Absaloms of this world can never see a David; they can see only Saul."

"And the pure heart?" asked Zadok.

"Ah, now there is a rare thing indeed. How does a broken heart and a broken will handle an Absalom? The way it handled a Saul? It will soon be ours to know, Zadok!

"You and I were not privileged to be there when David came to his hour with Saul. We are privileged to be present in his hour with Absalom. I for one intend to watch this unfolding drama very closely; and in so doing I have the good expectation that I will learn a lesson or two. Mark my words, David will work his way through this thing, and he will pass this test with the selfsame grace he displayed in his youth."

"And Absalom?"

"Absalom?

"In a few hours he may very well be my king, is that not your point?"

"There is that possibility," replied Zadok, almost with humor.

Nathan laughed. "If Absalom gains the throne may heaven have mercy on all the Sauls, Davids *and* Absaloms of the realm!

"In my judgment our young Absalom will make a splendid Saul," continued Nathan as he turned and strolled down the long corridor.

"Yes. A splendid Saul. For in every way but age and position, Absalom is already a Saul."

Chapter XXV

"I thank you for coming, Zadok."

"My king."

"You are a priest of God: Could you tell me a story of long ago?"

"What story, my king?"

"Do you know the story of Moses?"

"I do."

"Tell it to me."

"It is long; shall I tell it all?"

"No, not all."

"Then what part?"

"Tell me about Korah's rebellion."

The high priest stared at David with eyes burning. David stared back, his also ablaze. The two men understood.

"I shall tell you the story of Korah's rebellion, and of Moses' behavior in the midst of that rebellion.

"Many men have heard the story of Moses. He is the supreme example of the

Lord's anointed. God's true government rests upon a man, no, upon the contrite heart of a man. There is no form or order to God's government; there is only a man with a contrite heart. Moses was such a man.

"Korah was not such a man, although he was the first cousin of Moses. Korah wanted the authority Moses had. One peaceful morning, Korah awoke. There was no discord among God's people that morning, but before the day was over he had found 252 men to agree with his charges against Moses."

"Then there were problems in the nation when Moses ruled?" asked David.

"There are always problems in kingdoms," replied Zadok. "Always. Furthermore, the ability to be able to see those problems is a cheap gift, indeed."

David smiled and asked, "But Zadok, you know there have been unjust kingdoms and unjust rulers and pretenders and liars who have ruled and governed. How can a simple people tell which is a kingdom with faults, but led by men of God, and which is a kingdom unworthy of men's submission? How can a people know?"

David stopped; he realized that he had hit upon what he wished most of all to know. Heavily, he spoke again. "And the king— how can he know? Can he know if he is just? Can he know if the charges are of great worth? Are there signs?" David's final words were anxious.

"You are looking for some list let down from heaven, David. Even if there were such a list, even if there were a way to know, wicked men would arrange their kingdoms to fit the list! And if there were a list and a good man filled it to perfection, there would be those declaring he had fulfilled not one qualification listed therein. You underestimate the human heart, David."

"Then how shall the people know?"

"They shall not."

"You mean that in the midst of a hundred voices making a thousand claims, the simple people of God have no assurance of who is truly anointed to bear God's authority and who is not?"

"They shall never be certain."

"Who, then, can know?"

"God always knows—but He does not tell."

"Then is there no hope for those who must follow unworthy men?"

"Their grandchildren will be able to see the matter clearly. *They* will know. But those caught up in the drama? They shall never be certain. Nonetheless, a good thing will come from it all."

"What is that?"

"As surely as the sun rises, men's hearts will be tested. Despite the many claims— and counter claims—the hidden motives within the hearts of all those who are involved will be revealed. This may not seem important in the eyes of men, but in the eyes of God, and angels, such things are central. The heart must out. God will see to it."

"I despise such tests," replied David wearily. "I hate such nights as this one. Yet He seems to send many, many things into my life to test this heart of mine. Once more, this night, I find my heart is on trial.

"Zadok, there is something that bothers me above all else. Perhaps God *is* finished

with me. Is there not some way for me to
know?"

"I know of no other ruler in all history
who would even ask the question, good
king. Most other men would have ripped
their opponent—or even their imagined
opponent—to shreds by now. But to
answer your question, I know of no way
for you to be certain that God is—or is
not—finished with you."

David sighed, and choked back a sob.
"Then continue with the story. Korah had
252 followers, did he? What happened
next?"

"Korah approached Moses and Aaron
with his troop. He informed Moses that he
had no right to all the authority he
exercised."

"Well, we Hebrews are consistent, aren't
we?" laughed David.

"No, the heart of man is consistent,
David," replied Zadok.

"Tell me, what was Moses' response to
Korah?"

"At 40, Moses had been an arrogant, self-
willed man, not unlike Korah. What he
might have done at 40, I cannot say. At
80, he was a broken man. He was...."

"The meekest man who ever lived," interrupted David.

"The man who carries the rod of God's authority should be. Otherwise God's people will live in terror. Yes, a broken man faced Korah. And I believe you already know what Moses did, David. He did...nothing."

"Nothing. Ah, what a man."

"He fell on his face before God. That is all he did."

"Why did he do that, Zadok?"

"David, you of all men must know. Moses knew God alone had put him in charge of Israel. There was nothing that needed to be done. Those 253 men would seize the kingdom—or God would vindicate Moses. Moses knew that."

"Men would find it hard to imitate such a life, would they not? A fake surely could not fake such surrender, could he? But tell me, how did God vindicate Moses?"

"Moses told the men to return the next day with censers and incense...and God would decide the issue."

"So!" cried David. "So!" he exclaimed

again even louder. "Sometimes God *does* tell," he said excitedly. "What happened next?"

"Korah and two of his friends were swallowed by the earth. The other 250 died by...."

"Never mind. Suffice it to say that Moses was proven to be in authority...by God! God *did* tell! The people knew who really had authority from God, and at last, Moses had rest."

"No, David. He did not find rest, and the people were not satisfied with God's answer! The very next day the whole congregation murmured against Moses and would all have died perhaps, except for the prayers of Moses."

"And men fight to become kings!" David shook his head in perplexity.

Zadok paused, then continued: "David, I perceive you are torn by the question of what is true authority and what is not. You want to know what to do with a rebellion, if indeed it is a rebellion and not the hand of God. I trust you will find the only pure thing to do and do it. Thereby you will teach us all.

The door opened. Abishai rushed in.
"Good king! Your son, your own flesh and
blood, has proclaimed himself *king* in
Hebron. At first impression, it seems all
Israel has gone over to him. He plans to
take the throne. He marches toward
Jerusalem. Some of the men closest to you
have gone over to him."

David walked away. He spoke something
to himself but beyond the ears of any
other. "Israel's third king? Do true leaders
of the Kingdom of God come about
thusly?"

Zadok, not certain if he should be hearing
David's words or not, spoke out. "My
king?"

David turned, his eyes moist.

"At last," said David quietly, "at last this
matter will be resolved. Perhaps tomorrow
someone besides God will know."

"Perhaps," said Zadok, "but perhaps not.
Such questions may be debated even after
we are all dead."

"That might still be tomorrow," laughed
David. "Go, Abishai, tell Joab. You will
find him in the turret of the east wall."

Abishai departed as he had entered, in haste and in fury.

"I wonder, Zadok," mused David, "if a man can force God into a position where He *must* tell."

Chapter XXVI

Abishai rushed across the courtyard into the open door at the base of the east rampart and charged up the spiral staircase. Inside, at the top of the stairs, Joab stared down at Abishai, reached for a torch and began rushing down. In the flickering light of the torches, they met, each studying the face of the other intently. Abishai spoke.

"Have you heard, Joab?"

"Heard! 'Tis midnight, yet half the city is awake with the word. How can it be, Abishai—a son against his own father!"

"When kingdoms are vulnerable, men see queer sights," responded Abishai with a distant stare.

"And will sacrifice anything to satisfy ambition," added Jaob angrily. "What think you of these things, Abishai?"

"What think I?" responded Abishai, matching Joab's anger with his own rage. "This! Absalom has no authority in the kingdom. He holds no power, no office, yet he has risen up to divide the kingdom. He has raised his hand against the very anointed of God—against David! David— who has never done or spoken one evil word against him.

"What think I?" Abishai's voise rose toward a crescendo. "This: If Abaslom, who has no authority, will commit this deed; if Absalom, who is nothing, will divide the very kingdom of God;" his voice now rolled like thunder, "man, if Absalom will do these evil things *now*, what in the name of sanity might that man do if he be *king*?"

Chapter XXVII

David and Zadok were alone once more.

"And now, what shall you do, David? In your youth, you spoke no word against an unworthy king. What shall you do now with an equally unworthy youth?"

"As I said," replied David, "these are the times I hate the most, Zadok. Nonetheless, against all reason, I judge my own heart first and rule against its interests. I shall do what I did under Saul. I shall leave the destiny of the Kingdom in God's hands alone. It may be that He is finished with me. Perhaps I have sinned too greatly and am no longer worthy to lead. Only God knows if that is true, and it seems He will not tell." Then, clenching his fist, yet with a touch of wry humor in his voice, he added emphatically, "But today I shall give circumstances ample space for this untelling God of ours to be found out. I know of no other way to bring about such an extraordinary event except by doing *nothing*! The throne is not mine. Not to have, not to take, not to protect, and not to keep.

"I shall leave the city. The throne is the Lord's. So is the kingdom. I will not hinder God. No obstacle, no activity on my part lies in the space between God and His will. He has no hindrance to prevent Him from His will. If I am not to be King, our God will find no difficulties in making Absalom to be Israel's king. Now it is possible. God shall be God!"

The true king turned and walked quietly out of the throne room, out of the palace, out of the city. He walked and he walked...

Into the bosoms of all men whose hearts are pure.

Well, dear reader, the time has come for us to say goodbye once more. I will leave you to your thoughts and to reflection on the hidden motives of your own heart.

Oh, by the way, the players are working on a love story, perhaps we may see it together whenever it is performed.

I trust, then, by the mercy of God, we shall meet again.

Gene Edwards was born and raised in Texas, the son of an oil field roughneck. He was converted to Christ in his junior year in college. He graduated from East Texas State University in Commerce, Texas at the age of 18, with majors in English literature and history. His first year of postgraduate work was taken at the Baptist Seminary in Ruschlikon, Switzerland. He received his masters degree in theology from Southwestern Baptist Theological Seminary in Ft. Worth, Texas at the age of 22. He served as a Southern Baptist pastor, and then as an evangelist, for 10 years. He and his wife, Helen, now make their home in New England; his ministry includes conferences on the deeper Christian life and on living that life in the context of a practical experience of church life.

If you have enjoyed *A Tale of Three Kings,* you will want to read *The Divine Romance.* A masterfully told story, a magnificent saga that will take your breath away. Here is an incomparable love story—told in almost childlike simplicity, yet revealing some of the deepest truths of the Christian faith. Readers everywhere have acclaimed *The Divine Romance* as one of the finest pieces of Christian literature of our times.

CHRISTIAN BOOKS PUBLISHING HOUSE

BOOKS BY GENE EDWARDS

THE DIVINE ROMANCE

The most powerful, arresting book we have ever published. With a might and beauty that sweeps from eternity to eternity, here is, truly, the greatest love story ever told. If you have any interest at all in the deeper Christian life, then, by all means, read this book. Rarely, if ever, has the depth and mystery of Christ been put so simply, yet so profoundly and so breathtakingly beautiful.

A TALE OF THREE KINGS

A book beloved around the world. A dramatically told tale of Saul, David and Absalom, on the subject of brokenness. A book used in the healing of the lives of many Christians who have been devastated by church splits and by injuries suffered at the hands of other Christians.

OUR MISSION

A group of Christian young men in their early twenties met together for a weekend retreat to hear Gene Edwards speak. Unknown to them, they were about to pass through a catastrophic split. These messages were delivered to prepare those young men spiritually for the inevitable disaster facing them. Edwards presents the standard of the first century believers and how those believers walked when passing through similar crises. A remarkable statement on how a Christian is to conduct himself in times of strife, division and crisis. A book every Christian, every minister, every worker will need at one time or another in his life.

INWARD JOURNEY

Crossing time and space, a young man named Chris Young learns the Christian meaning of transformation. A study in suffering, pain and the ways of God in our lives.

LETTERS TO A DEVASTATED CHRISTIAN

Gene Edwards writes a series of letters to a Christian who has been deeply damaged by a crisis in the group he has been part of. A book that has brought help, counsel and healing to many hurt Christians.

BOOKS BY MADAM GUYON

EXPERIENCING THE DEPTHS OF JESUS CHRIST

Guyon's first and best known book. One of the most influential pieces of Christian literature ever penned on the deeper Christian life. Among the multitudes of people who have read this book and urged others to read it are: John Wesley, Adoniram Judson, Watchman Nee, Jesse Penn-Lewis, Zinzendorf, and the Quakers. A timeless piece of literature that has been on the "must read" list of Christians for 300 years.

THE STORY OF MADAME GUYON'S LIFE, by T.C. Upham

If you enjoy reading Jeanne Guyon's writings, you will wish to read the story of her life. Through the centuries a multitude of Christians have held it to be the most outstanding life story of any Christian woman in church history. Truly one of Christendom's best known and most frequently read biographies.

Her well-known autobiography details her life only to about 40, whereas she became an internationally known figure and spiritual influence in Europe after that time. Some of the most significant aspects of her life story are not included in her remarkable autobiography. T.C. Upham's history of her life, on the other hand, recounts her fame in the Court of Louis XIV, her clash with Bossuet, her trial, the international storm created by Fenelon's clash with Bossuet over her teachings, her imprisonment in the dungeon of Vincennes, her four years as a prisoner in the infamous Bastille.

One of the half dozen truly great Christian biographies.

THE SPIRITUAL ADVENTURE

This book could well be called volume two of EXPERIENCING THE DEPTHS OF JESUS CHRIST. Here is a look at the experiences a more advanced and faithful Christian might encounter in his/her walk with the Lord. Without question, next to EXPERIENCING THE DEPTHS, here is Mme. Jeanne Guyon's best book.

UNION WITH GOD

Written as a companion book to EXPERIENCING THE DEPTHS OF JESUS CHRIST, and includes 22 of her poems.

SONG OF SONGS
GENESIS

Jeanne Guyon wrote a commentary on the Bible; here are two of those books. SONG OF SONGS has been popular through the centuries and has greatly influenced several other well-known commentaries on the Song of Songs.

THE SPIRITUAL LETTERS OF MADAME GUYON

Here is spiritual counseling at its very best. There is a Christ-centeredness to Jeanne Guyon's counsel that is rarely, if ever, seen in Christian literature.

THE WAY OUT

A spiritual study of Exodus as seen from "the interior way."

THE BOOK OF JOB

Guyon looks at the life of Job from the view of the deeper Christian life.

CHRIST OUR REVELATION

A profound and spiritual look at the book of Revelation.

CLASSICS ON THE DEEPER CHRISTIAN LIFE

PRACTICING HIS PRESENCE

The monumental seventeenth century classic by Brother Lawrence, now in modern English. One of the most read and recommended Christian books of the last 300 years.

The twentieth century missionary, Frank Laubach, while living in the Philippines, sought to put into practice Brother Lawrence's words. Included in this edition are excerpts from Frank Laubach's diary. This book is a Christian classic by *any* standard; this book consistently shows up on more "top-ten must-read" book recommendations list than any other piece of Christian literature in print.

THE SPIRITUAL GUIDE

At the time Jeanne Guyon was teaching in the royal court of Louis XIV (in France), a man named Michael Molinos was leading a spiritual revival among the clergy and laymen of Rome! He actually lived in the Vatican, his influence reaching to all Italy and beyond. The great, the near great, the unknown sought him out for spiritual counsel. He was the spiritual director of many of the illuminaries of the seventeenth century. He wrote THE SPIRITUAL GUIDE to meet the need of a growing hunger for spiritual direction. The book was, for a time, probably the most popular book in Europe, but was later banned and condemned to be burned. The author was convicted and sentenced to a dungeon after one of the most sensational trials in European history.

Here, in modern English, is that remarkable book.

CHURCH HISTORY

These two books bring to bear a whole new perspective on church life.

THE EARLY CHURCH

This book tells, in a "you are there" approach, what it was like to be a Christian in the first century church, recounting the events from Pentecost to Antioch. By Gene Edwards.

THE TORCH OF THE TESTIMONY

John W. Kennedy tells the little known, almost forgotten, story of evangelical Christians during the dark ages.

If you are just getting acquainted with books on the deeper Christian life, we would like to suggest what may be the best approach to reading books on this subject. There is not a great deal of literature available in this area of the Christian walk, so you will wish to make the most of what is available.

We recommend that you begin your reading with THE DIVINE ROMANCE. Follow with EXPERIENCING THE DEPTHS OF JESUS CHRIST and PRACTICING HIS PRESENCE. THE DIVINE ROMANCE will stir and give insight and prepare you for the practical and spiritual help found in the other two books.

Two other books which complement EXPERIENCING THE DEPTHS OF JESUS CHRIST are UNION WITH GOD and THE SPIRITUAL GUIDE.

You will also find real profit in reading THE SPIRITUAL LETTERS of Jeanne Guyon and THE SPIRITUAL LETTERS of Fenelon. Many of the questions and problems of your daily walk with Christ and your relationship with others are dealt with in these two books.

For insight into brokenness and to see just what the heart of a man of God should be, the beautiful A TALE OF THREE KINGS is a book you will want to read again and again. If you would like to know more about the ways and purposes of the cross, suffering and transformation (which must come into the life of all Christians), then you will want to read THE INWARD JOURNEY.

DIVINE LIFE might be looked upon as a technical explanation of the human spirit and its difference from the human soul, but having read this book, you will be pleased to know more about the spiritual process going on inside you. This book is a great help to Christians in their quest to get a handle on their spirit.

THE EARLY CHURCH, Volume I, the story of the body of Christ from Pentecost to Antioch, will give you insight into what "church life" meant in the first century.

THE TORCH OF THE TESTIMONY tells the story of the church and church life as it survived during the dark ages and beyond.

The following prices are for the year 1986 only; please write for our catalog for price update and for new releases.

A Tale of Three Kings
   (Edwards) 5.95
The Divine Romance (Edwards) ....(10.95 hb) 7.95pb
Experiencing the Depths of
   Jesus Christ (Guyon)......................................5.95
The Inward Journey (Edwards) 5.95
Letters to a Devastated Christian
   (Edwards) 3.95
Our Mission (Edwards)...7.95
The Early Church (Edwards) 5.95
Practicing His Presence (Lawrence) 5.95
Union with God (Guyon) 5.95
The Spiritual Adventure (Guyon)...........................6.95
The Spiritual Guide (Molinos) 5.95
Torch of the Testimony (Kennedy).........................6.95
The Autobiography of Mme. Guyon 5.95
Guyon's Commentaries:
   Genesis..5.95
   Exodus (The Way Out)..................................6.95
   Song of Songs..5.95
   Job..7.95
   Revelation (Christ Our Revelation)...................7.95
The Biography of Mme. Guyon (Upham)................8.95

Christian Books
Publishing House
Box 959
Gardiner, Maine 04345
207-737-8267
Visa-Mastercard accepted